WARSHIP PICTORIAL #4

UNITED STATES NAVY
USS TEXAS BB-35

Steve Wiper & Tom Flowers

March 3, 1914 - The USS Texas *makes speed during the builder's acceptance trials.*

CLASSIC WARSHIPS PUBLISHING

P. O. Box 57591 • Tucson, AZ. 85732 • USA
Web Site: www.classicwarships.com • Ph/Fx (520)748-2992
Copyright © December 1999 • Revised May 2006
ISBN 0-9654829-3-6
Printed by Arizona Lithographers, Tucson, Arizona

USS TEXAS BB-35
New York Class Battleship
Operational history

1910

June 24 - US Congress authorized Battleship number 34 and 35 as the first 14in gunned ships in the US Navy and the world.

1911

Officially named USS *Texas* by the Secretary of the Navy, von L. Meyer.
April 17 - Keel laid down at Newport News Shipbuilding and Dry Dock Company of Virginia.

1912

May 18 - Launched. Event was recorded on film and is one of the first motion pictures of the launching of a US Navy ship.

1914

March 12 - Commissioned, with Capt. Albert W. Grant as the ship's first commanding officer.
May 19/November 23 - Supported US occupation forces at Vera Cruz, Mexico during that country's civil unrest.
Summer - Began shakedown cruise from Bremerton to New York City via the Panama Canal.

1915-16

Engaged in fleet tactics and battle maneuvers from the New England Coast to the Caribbean Sea.

1917

Was a member of Battleship Force of the Atlantic Fleet, based on the York River at Yorktown, Virginia.
April 6 - America enters the First World War on the side of the Allies.
September 27 - Runs aground off Block Island, Long Island Sound. After lightening, the ship is pulled free by her sister ship, USS *New York*. Damage to the hull was considerable.

1918

January 30 - With repairs completed, departed for England
February 11 - Arrived at Scapa Flow and joined additional US battleships to form the Sixth Battle Squadron of the British Grand Fleet.
In the ship's only engagement of WWI, successfully evaded single torpedo attack from enemy submarine and unsuccessfully returned fire.
November 11 - World War I ended with the signing of the armistice.
November 21 - Escorted the German High Seas Fleet to the Firth of Forth, England for their surrender.

December 1 - Sails with five other US battleships for the United States via Portsmouth, England and Brest, France.
December 26 - Arrived in New York and passed in review of Secretary of the Navy, Josephus Daniels and thousands of cheering onlookers.

1919

March 9 - Launched the first successful flight of an aircraft (Sopwith Camel) from a battleship.
May 8/27 - Participated as a station ship during the US Navy's first trans-Atlantic seaplane crossing: New York to Portugal.
July 14 - Sailed for the West Coast and a transfer to the Pacific Fleet.

1924

Early - Transferred back to the Atlantic Fleet and docked for overhaul.
June/August - Served as a training ship for Midshipmen from the Naval Academy at Annapolis.
November 25 - Sinks with gun fire the incomplete battleship Washington BB-47, in accordance with the terms of the Washington Naval Treaty of 1922. Extensive armor strength testing done.

1925

Spring - Began extensive and lengthy modernization and overhaul at Norfolk Navy Yard. Received new masting and superstructure, additional armor, anti torpedo bulges and new oil-fired boilers.

1927

September 1 - Became flagship of Admiral C.F. Hughes, Commander-in-Chief, United States Fleet.

1928

January - Ferried President Herbert Hoover to the Pan-American Conference at Havana, Cuba

1931

Spring - Underwent refit at New York Navy Yard.
Winter - Arrived at San Diego to assume duty as Flagship of Battle Division I.

1932/1936

Engaged in numerous maneuvers and drills with the US Navy. Also served as good will ambassador on tours of foreign ports and as a receptionist at home.

1937

Reassigned to the East Coast as Flagship of Training Detachment, US Fleet. Later became Flagship of the newly created US Atlantic Squadron.

1939

January 4 - Receives first commercial radar aboard a US Navy ship.
September 1 - War in Europe breaks out with German attack on Poland.
September 6 - Becomes part of the Neutrality Patrol established along the East Coast to protect US and other neutral shipping. A 300 mile cordon is patrolled from Newfoundland to Trinidad.

1940

September 16 - In alliance with the Canadian and Royal Navies, extended patrol duties to the mid Atlantic.

1941

February 1 - In Guantanamo Bay, Cuba, hosts ceremonies on her fantail as the First Marine Brigade is redesignated the First Marine Division.
April - Enters Norfolk Navy Yard for refit and war preparations.
June 20 - After returning to Atlantic convoy support, evades torpedo attack from German submarine U-203
December 7 - Anchored at Casco Bay, Maine.

1942

January/February - Stationed at Hvalfjord, Iceland to help counter the threat of the German battleship, Tirpitz.
April - Escorted troop convoy to Panama Canal.
May - Escorted convoy to West Africa.
June - Escorted Troop Convoy to Greenock, Scotland.
August - Assigned to naval task force scheduled for the invasion of North Africa "Operation Torch" and underwent training exercises.
October 23 - Sailed with the North Africa force as flagship for Rear Admiral Kelly.
November 7 - Arrived off Mehedia, Morocco and began shore bombardment the following afternoon supporting troops that had landed that morning. War correspondent Walter Cronkite was on board covering the landing operation.
November 10 - Engaged Vichy French reinforcement convoys.
November 26 - Returned to Norfolk Navy Yard for refit.

1943

January 25/February 14 - Departed New York as flagship of round trip convoy escort force, screening troopships bound for Casablanca.
April 29/June 1 - Escorted Convoy UGF-8 again to Casablanca and returned to New York.
August 21/September 21 - Entered a third mission to Casablanca, escorting supply ships and 64,000 troops.
October/November - Led protection forces for northern convoy bound for Scotland.

December 29 - Began convoy run with materials and men bound for Clyde, Scotland, there to be amassed for an impending European invasion.

1944

February 14 - Returned from Scotland and immediately entered Boston Naval Yard for repairs and refit.
February 25 - Began short training program at Casco Bay.
April 6 - Sailed with supply convoy bound for Scotland. Upon arrival, entered Belfast Lough, Northern Ireland for installations of new electronic equipment.
May 19 - Visited by the Supreme Allied Commander, General Dwight D. Eisenhower
June 6 - As flagship of Allied bombardment force, begins early morning shelling of Omaha Beach, opening the largest amphibious assault in history: The Invasion of Normandy.
June 7 - Continued with strategic shelling program and supplied isolated Rangers at Pionte du Hoc.
June 9 - Took brief respite to England to replenish supplies.
June 25 - During bombardment off the coast of Cherbourg, came under direct fire from German shore battery "Hamburg". Received two hits from 280mm guns. Only one shell exploded, inflicting the only casualty in the ships war-time career, the helmsman. 13 were wounded.
July 15 - After repairs to recent battle damage, sailed to the Mediterranean to take part in the invasion of South France.
August 15/16 - Bombarded enemy shore positions at Saint-Tropez which resulted in an unopposed Allied landing.
September 14 - Arrived at New York Naval Yard for overhaul including the replacement of the badly worn 14 in gun barrel linings.
November 10 - After overhaul and brief shakedown cruise, leaves Casco Bay in company of USS Missouri and Arkansas, bound for the Pacific.
December 9 - Via the Panama Canal and after a stop at San Pedro, California, ports at Pearl Harbor for preparations for action against the Pacific enemy.

1945

January 9 - Departed Pearl Harbor en route to the Carolina Islands.
January 30 - Arrived at Ulithi Atoll under the flag of Rear Admiral Fisher, Battleship Division Five and participated in subsequent landing rehearsals.
February 15 - Arrived at Iwo Jima and began pre-invasion bombardment of enemy held island.
February 16/23 - Continued bombardment and anti-aircraft support until the fall of Mt. Suribachi.
March 7 - Returned to Ulithi Atoll for preparations for the next major campaign.
March 21 - Sailed as part of Task Force 54 for the invasion of Okinawa.
March 25 - Covered mine sweeping operations upon arrival.
April 1 - Participated as part of a diversionary action on the southern beach to mis-lead actual landing location.

April 16 - During bombardment and anti-aircraft operations, destroyed attacking "kamikaze".

May 14 - Left Okinawa campaign for maintenance and repairs.

May 17 - Arrived at San Pedro Bay, Philippines. After servicing, assigned patrol duties and carried out battle practice.

August 23 - Upon secession of hostilities, sailed for the United States, with brief stops at Buckner Bay, Okinawa and Pearl Harbor.

October 15 - Entered San Pedro, California with returning combat veterans.

October 27 - Hosts "Navy Day" celebration on board, with over 13,000 visitors.

October 30 - Left San Pedro, California on the first of three "Magic Carpet" runs to the Pacific, ferrying over 4,200 men back to the United States.

1946

January 21 - After completion of third "Magic Carpet" mission, left San Pedro for the East Coast via the Panama Canal.

February 13 - Arrived at Norfolk, Virginia and shortly afterwards underwent preparations for deactivation and storage at Hawkins Point, Maryland

June 18 - Decommissioned and placed officially in reserve.

1948

January 15 - Preparations began for last campaign.

March 17 - Began transfer voyage to new anchorage at Galveston, Texas.

April 20 - Moored in the slip at the San Jacinto State Park.

April 21: "Texas Independence Day" - was presented to the state of Texas and recommissioned as the Flagship of the Texas Navy. Began new career as a naval museum.

1988

December 13 - Towed 56 miles from her birth to Todd Dry Dock & Shipyard of Galveston for much needed repairs.

1990

February 23 - Moved to Greens Bayou for further reconstruction.

September 8 - Returned to San Jacinto State Park and resumed her career as a living memorial and a tribute to the United States Navy and all American Armed Forces personnel.

HONORS

BATTLE STARS	SERVICE AWARDS
NORTH AFRICAN OCCUPATION Algeria-Morocco landings: November 8/11 1942	**MEXICAN SERVICE MEDAL** May 26/August 8, 1914; October 9/November 4, 1914
INVASION OF NORMANDY June 6/25, 1945	**WORLD WAR I VICTORY MEDAL** Grand Fleet Clasp - February 11/November 11, 1918 Armed Guard Clasp - August 20/November 11, 1918
INVASION OF SOUTHERN FRANCE August 15/September 28, 1944	
IWO JIMA OPERATION Assault & Occupation: February 16/February7, 1945	**AMERICAN DEFENSE SERVICE MEDAL** July 17/25 1941; October 13/November 26, 1941
OKINAWA OPERATION Assault & Occupation: March 25/May 14, 1945	**NAVY OCCUPATION SERVICE MEDAL (ASIA)** September 2/23, 1945

October 2, 1913: Newport News Shipyard - Activity is everywhere as workmen "finish-out" the Texas. *Much was still needed to be done. Notice how high the ship was ridding in the water.*

January 3, 1914: Newport News, Virginia - Only two months are left before her commissioning. The lighter colored lines on the hull are primer paint covering welded seams. The final coat of Standard Navy Gray will be applied soon over the entire ship. The white canvas tents under the 14in barrels of #3 turret are temporary covers over the machinery spaces. When the interior work is completed, the deck will be finished to strength. At the very stern, sits the #21 5in gun, later found to be unusable in all but the calmest of seas.

The two forward casemate 5in/51s (the two sternmost also) were lightly protected by hinged panels, which dropped down in battle to give the guns a full arc of fire. These two gun positions forward were also found to be unusable because of wetness. The ship carries only one anchor on the starboard side.

March 28, 1914 - Although the Texas *is brand new, preparations are being made for her immediate contribution in the US conflict with Mexico. Just behind the conning tower, sits the bridge position: a completely open platform with only canvas for top and side protection. Rangefinder positions atop the cage masts had only canvas for tops also.*

July, 1919 - Rare <u>aerial</u> photograph from this time period shows the relative simplicity of early battleships decks. The teakwood overlay was unpainted. Numerous "mushroom" vents help relieve the high temperatures below decks, especially in the machinery spaces. Skylights mounted on the center line, are open to provide light and ventilation. Notice in the right lower corner, the casemate doors on the after 5in/51 are lowered.

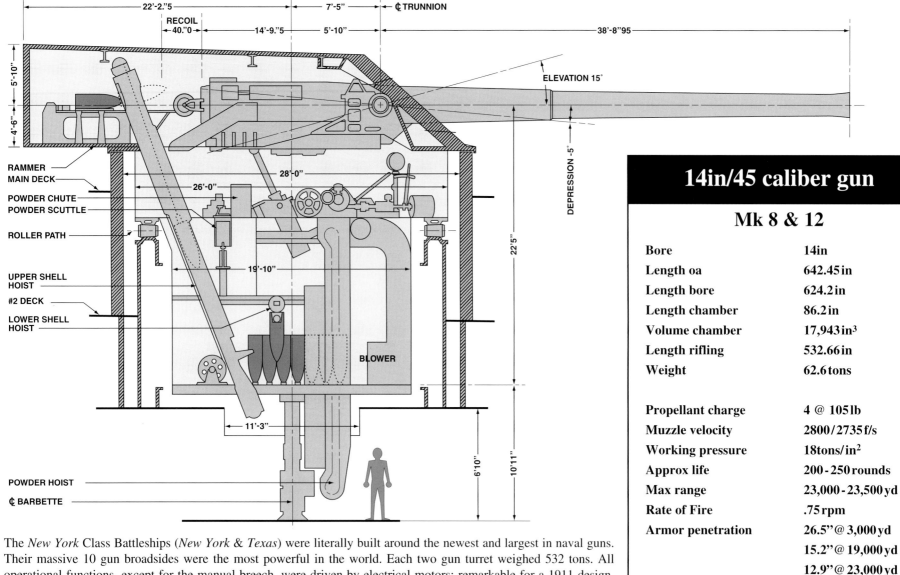

14in/45 caliber gun

Mk 8 & 12

Bore	14in
Length oa	642.45in
Length bore	624.2in
Length chamber	86.2in
Volume chamber	17,943in^3
Length rifling	532.66in
Weight	62.6tons
Propellant charge	4 @ 105lb
Muzzle velocity	2800/2735f/s
Working pressure	18tons/in^2
Approx life	200-250rounds
Max range	23,000-23,500yd
Rate of Fire	.75rpm
Armor penetration	26.5"@3,000yd
	15.2"@19,000yd
	12.9"@23,000yd
Weight projectile	AP - 1500lb
	HE - 1275lb

Texas was built with Mk8 14in/45 cal guns. In late 1944 she was refitted with the Mk12

The *New York* Class Battleships (*New York* & *Texas*) were literally built around the newest and largest in naval guns. Their massive 10 gun broadsides were the most powerful in the world. Each two gun turret weighed 532 tons. All operational functions, except for the manual breech, were driven by electrical motors; remarkable for a 1911 design. Turret training speed was 100° per minute in an arc of 300° (turret #3 @ 135° P&S). Gun elevation range was -5° to 15° at 4° per second. The *Texas* and *New York* were the only battleships to store and hoist their 14in ammunition in an inverted, nose down position, in cast iron cups. Although her guns were designed for ship to ship combat (which she never saw), the *Texas* made an excellent floating bombardment battery against enemy shore positions. During the Second World War at the beachheads of North Africa, Normandy, Southern France, Iwo Jima and Okinawa, the ship fired 4278 rounds at the enemy.

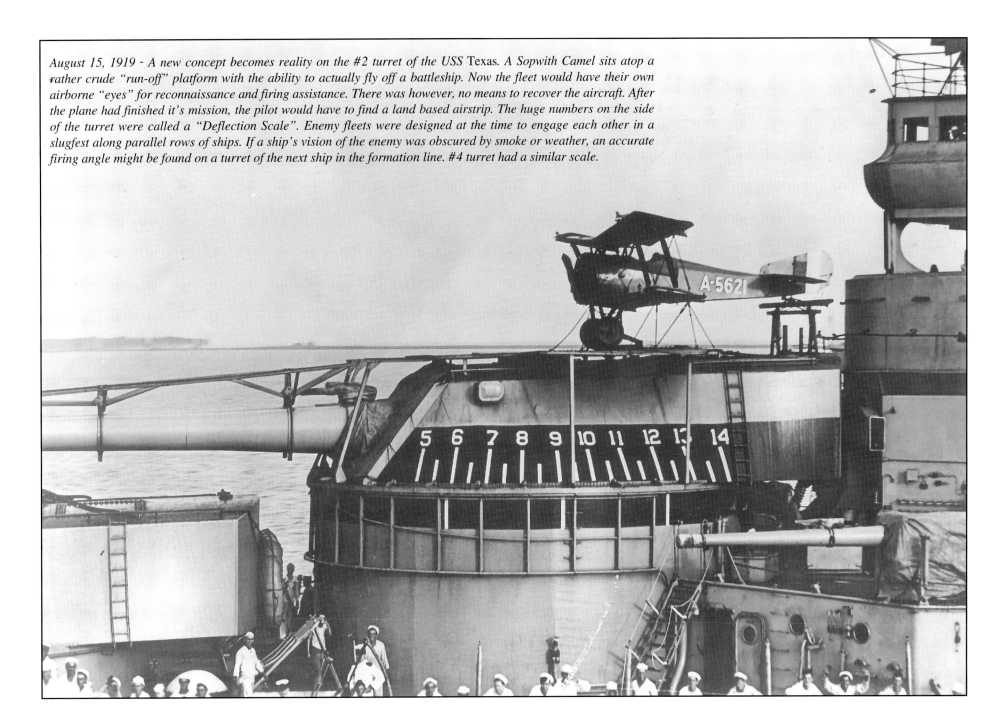

August 15, 1919 - A new concept becomes reality on the #2 turret of the USS Texas. A Sopwith Camel sits atop a rather crude "run-off" platform with the ability to actually fly off a battleship. Now the fleet would have their own airborne "eyes" for reconnaissance and firing assistance. There was however, no means to recover the aircraft. After the plane had finished it's mission, the pilot would have to find a land based airstrip. The huge numbers on the side of the turret were called a "Deflection Scale". Enemy fleets were designed at the time to engage each other in a slugfest along parallel rows of ships. If a ship's vision of the enemy was obscured by smoke or weather, an accurate firing angle might be found on a turret of the next ship in the formation line. #4 turret had a similar scale.

March-May 1919 - The Texas *gently cruises sometime during the aircraft testing, done mostly in Guantanamo Bay, Cuba. Apparent in this photo are a new, enclosed navigation station and a similar structure around the #2 cage mast. Both positions were designed to give navigation personnel a higher vantage point. She has also received additional 36in search lights. 5in guns at positions 1 & 2 have been removed.*

Circa 1920 - This undated photograph shows new 20ft rangefinders on the navigation bridge and on the #3 14in turret. The ship has received her first anti-aircraft weapons in the form of 3in/50cal single action guns, one of which can be spotted at the top of the boat crane. 5in guns at positions 3 & 4 are now gone.

Texas en route to Guantanamo Bay, Cuba for aircraft fly-off testing. She carries remnants of her WWI duty: the anti-splinter matting around the crane tops and the aft search light platform. Six-pointed stars help to keep the maze of antenna lines separated. The "range clock" on the aft cage mast was used to tell the ship behind in the battle line that the Texas "had found range with the enemy" and the dial would reflect that distance. Notice that the readout only goes to 10,000 yds; as gun ranges increased, the dial became worthless.

July 25, 1919 - Double ended trolleys slowly pull the Texas *through one of the great locks of the Panama Canal. The crew has turned out including a number of officers standing at the bow. The ship will transverse oceans and become a member of the Pacific Fleet for the next four years, carrying out routine maneuvers and training. The lower part of the fly-off platform on the barrels of #2 turret is not covered, showing only the flimsy bracing.*

November, 1926: Norfolk Navy Yard - After nearly two years of overhaul, the Texas *emerges as a state-of-the-art battleship. Her modernization was greatly influenced by the naval engagements of the First World War. A massive bulge was incorporated into the lower hull as a defense against the power of the modern torpedo, increasing the beam by almost 11 ft. Only 10 of the original 5 in/51 remain; six of those moved a deck higher to the enlarged command level. Heavier tripod masts now replace the cagemasts and atop the forward mast is the familiar "fighting top" found on US battleships of this era.*

5 in/51 caliber anti-destroyer gun

Scale 1/48

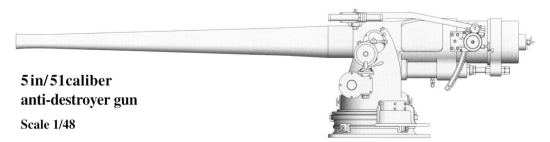

With new oil-fired boilers replacing the older coal-fired ones, all of the exhaust was now funneled through one stack. This made room for the addition of a second fire control position similar to the one on the foremast. 14in fire control was located in the round upper part, the lower area contained the 5in/51 fire control. The new mainmast aft contains four 36in searchlights and the motion picture projection booth below. The ships boats stacked amidship are 40ft and 50ft motor launches and a 26ft motor whaleboat on top. Hanging on davits aft, are 36ft rowing cutters.

To counter the rising threat of aerial attack, 3 in/50 cal anti-aircraft guns were mounted on the new command level: four each on the port & starboard, abreast the main superstructure. An enclosed navigation bridge has been erected around the foremast legs above the conning tower. The arms on the two cranes have been lengthened to handle the ship's aircraft as well as the small boats.

U.S.S. TEXAS.
NORFOLK NAVY YARD.

November 1926 - The Texas *now has a permanent Mk4 catapult for her spotting aircraft on turret #3. Since there are no hanger facilities, the aircraft are often stored on the catapult, as shown in the lower photograph.*

Late 1920s - The ship had a flag bridge added atop the navigation level and the rangefinder there was then moved to the top of the new flag bridge. The three aircraft are Chance-Vought O3U Corsairs, lashed to the catapult.

November 4, 1930: New York Navy Yard - Harbor tugs ease the Texas into port prior to her early 1931 refit. Both the navigation and the flag deck forward shielding have been constructed with parabolic wind deflectors. The idea being to create a wind tunnel which passed over deck personnel at the forward rail. The shape of these deflectors are defined through a specific mathematical formula.

June 21, 1937 - BB-35 passes through the Gatun Locks, Panama Canal en route to the Atlantic. Above the main fire control position on the foremast, a "bird bath" containing four 50cal machine guns adds to the anti-aircraft protection. Another "bird bath" sits on the mainmast top. The crew has turned out to help pilot the ship through the tight passageway.

3-IN. MOUNT, MARK 22 MOD. 4

3-IN. 50-CAL., D. P., SINGLE MOUNT, OPEN, PEDESTAL TYPE

ASSY. NO.	SKETCH NO.
448	107085
468	108309
470	108312
473	108327
483	138191

Note: Assembly number of mount is required for precise information.

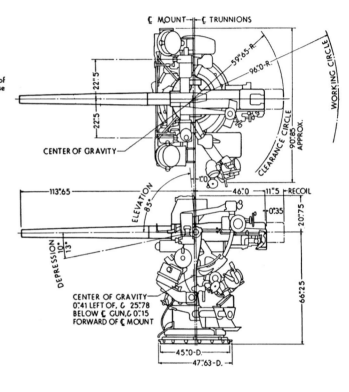

GUN—3"/50	
INSTALLATION FOR	MK. 21 MOD. 0 OR MK. 22 MOD. 0
	BB—CL—DE
SHIELD	NONE
	Weights below are approximate
TOTAL WEIGHT OF ASSEMBLY	7,200 TO 7,800 LBS.
OSCILLATING WEIGHT	3,600 TO 3,700 LBS.
RECOILING WEIGHT	1,850 LBS.
BRAKE LOAD	27,500 LBS.
TRUNNION PRESSURE HORIZ. FIRE	27,700 LBS.
TRUNNION PRESSURE 85° ELEV. FIRE	31,100 LBS.

3"/50, MARK 22 MOD. 4

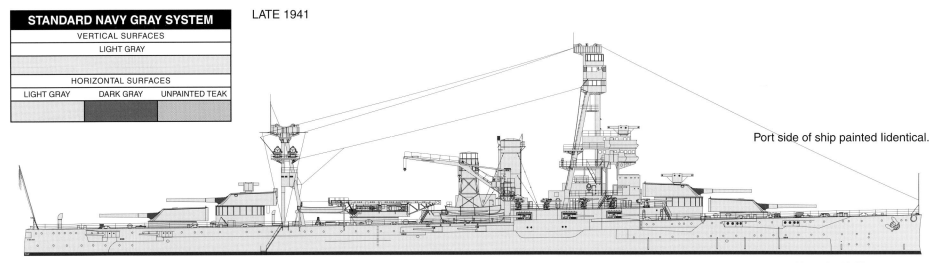

STANDARD NAVY GRAY SYSTEM		
VERTICAL SURFACES		
LIGHT GRAY		
HORIZONTAL SURFACES		
LIGHT GRAY	DARK GRAY	UNPAINTED TEAK

LATE 1941

Port side of ship painted Iidentical.

ship scale - 1/700

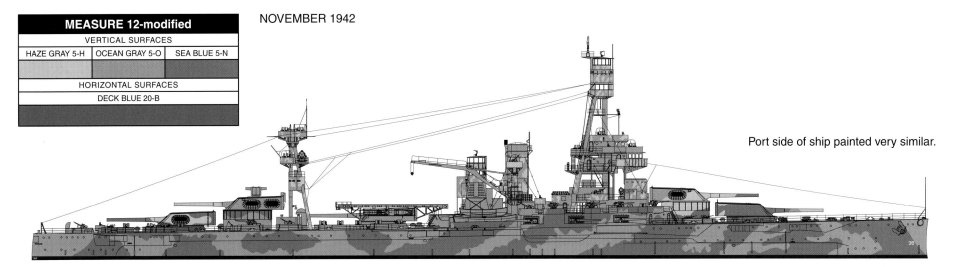

MEASURE 12-modified		
VERTICAL SURFACES		
HAZE GRAY 5-H	OCEAN GRAY 5-O	SEA BLUE 5-N
HORIZONTAL SURFACES		
DECK BLUE 20-B		

NOVEMBER 1942

Port side of ship painted very similar.

The USS Texas *was commissioned in 1914 with Standard Navy Gray paint. This paint was very light in shade and was the "standard" paint in the peace-time US Navy. The* Texas *carried more or less this scheme up to the US entry into the Second world War. It was around this time that the major participants in the war were spending increased efforts to design and test camouflage colors and patterns for their navy's ships. The United States developed hundreds of different designs and actually employed a wide variety of these for every ship and condition they were* expected to encounter. Camouflage is the attempt to alter an objects visibility during the time of most danger and is defined by two basic types: concealment and confusion. The former attempts to reduce the ship's visibility by coloring the ship similar to the background. The latter type attempts to confuse the viewer, making identification, speed and course more difficult to calculate. True color chips are found on the bottom of page 31.

The color intensity of all illustrations has been adjusted to maintain detail.

USS TEXAS BB-35

BOOKLET OF GENERAL PLANS DRAWINGS
1934
1/700 Scale

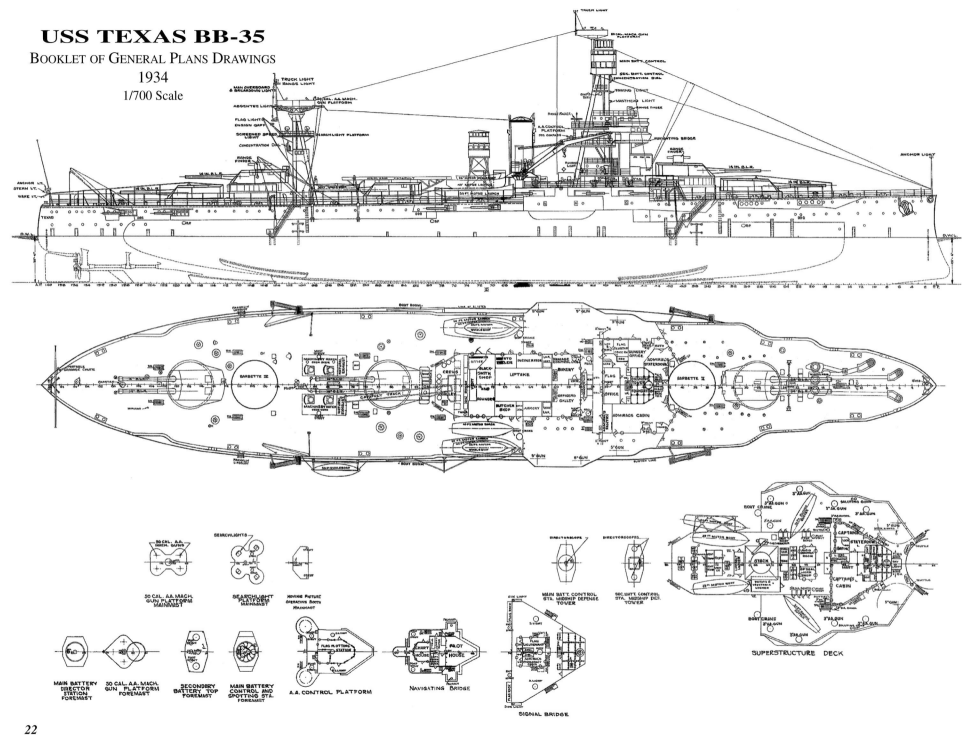

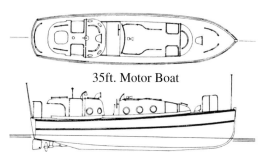

35ft. Motor Boat

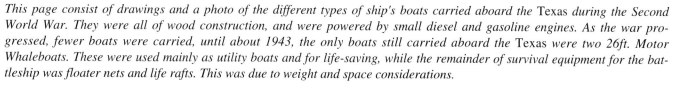

This page consist of drawings and a photo of the different types of ship's boats carried aboard the Texas during the Second World War. They were all of wood construction, and were powered by small diesel and gasoline engines. As the war progressed, fewer boats were carried, until about 1943, the only boats still carried aboard the Texas were two 26ft. Motor Whaleboats. These were used mainly as utility boats and for life-saving, while the remainder of survival equipment for the battleship was floater nets and life rafts. This was due to weight and space considerations.

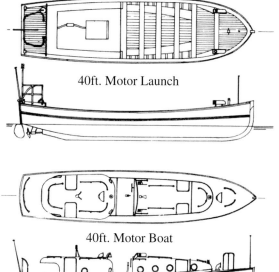

40ft. Motor Launch

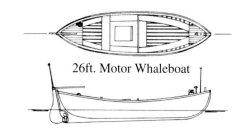

26ft. Motor Whaleboat

40ft. Motor Boat

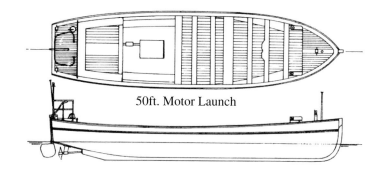

50ft. Motor Launch

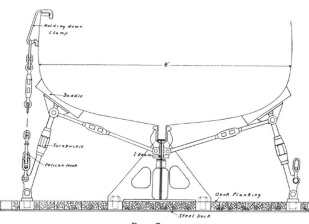

BOAT STOWAGE

The drawing to the left is a cross section showing the stowage of a ship's boat mounted to the deck. A long "I" beam ran the length of the boat, supporting the keel. The clamps, turnbuckle and pelican hooks on both sides, secured the boat to it's cradle during rough weather.

The drawing to the right is a cross section of a motor launch illustrating the construction of this type of boat. These methods were similar on all of the wooden boats of the US Navy during this period.

Both drawings are copied from US Navy manuals.

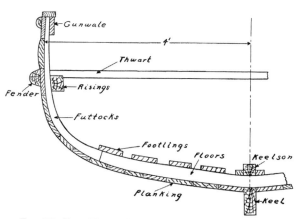

FIG. 122—HALF MIDSHIP SECTION OF MOTOR SAILING LAUNCH

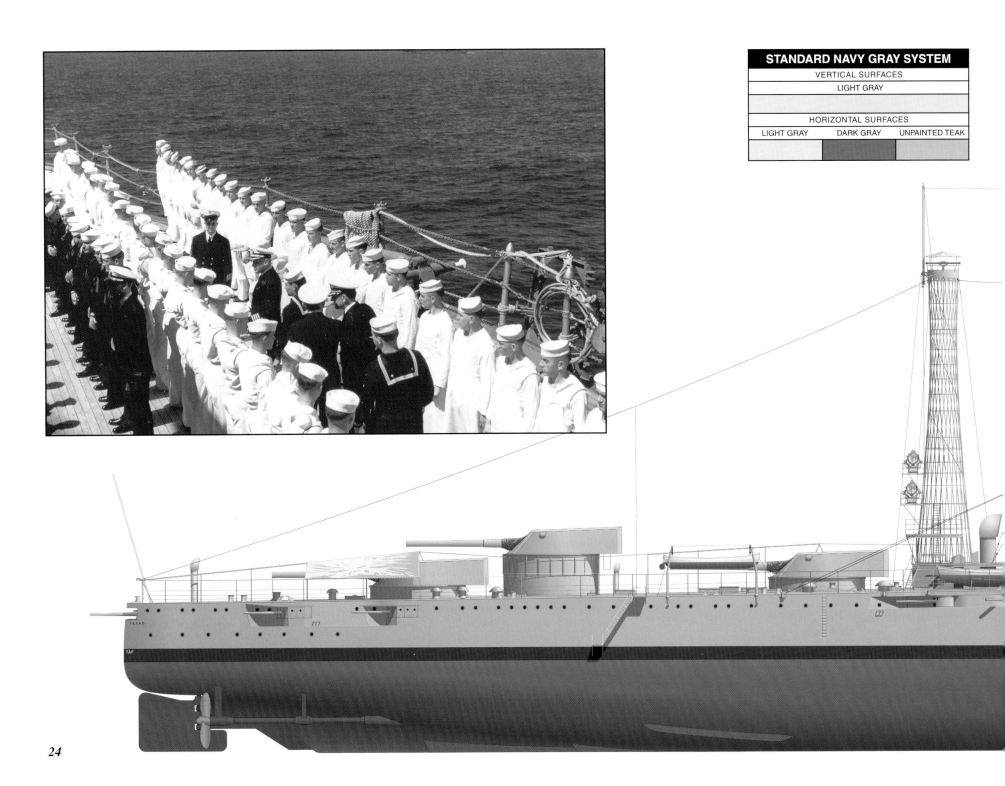

STANDARD NAVY GRAY SYSTEM

VERTICAL SURFACES		
LIGHT GRAY		
HORIZONTAL SURFACES		
LIGHT GRAY	DARK GRAY	UNPAINTED TEAK

USS TEXAS BB-35

March 1914

SCALE 1/350

Circa - 1938 - USS Texas, *flagship of the US Atlantic Fleet.*

July 4, 1938 - Signal flags flutter from the center line to help celebrate the nation's birthday. "Tropical tarps" are deployed on the forecastle and amidships to provide shade for the crew of a 30,000 ton steel skillet.

1938 - A interesting view looking forward from the aft movie projection room. The structure in the center is the midship defense tower accommodating main and secondary fire control. The ship's single funnel rises just behind, topped with a black band. The tall pipe on the left carries smoke away from the ship's incinerator. As a flagship, she has accommodations for the admiral and his staff, including staterooms, wardrooms and of course, the admiral's own launch, the covered 40ft boat second from the left. The captain's 36-footer is second from the right.

This, and the other color photographs are some of only a handful of color photos of the Texas, in her USN period, known to exist. Based on objects aboard, the photos are dated between January and August 1941. The January date is based on the Kingfisher airplane. The August date is based on the birdbath platform, atop the foremast. This was removed when she went into Norfolk Navy Yard, in August 1941. The birdbath platform was removed for the installation of the CXAM-1 radar antenna.

MEASURE 21
VERTICAL SURFACES
NAVY BLUE
HORIZONTAL SURFACES
DECK BLUE 20-B

USS TEXAS BB-35

Drawing Date: February 1945

SCALE 1/350

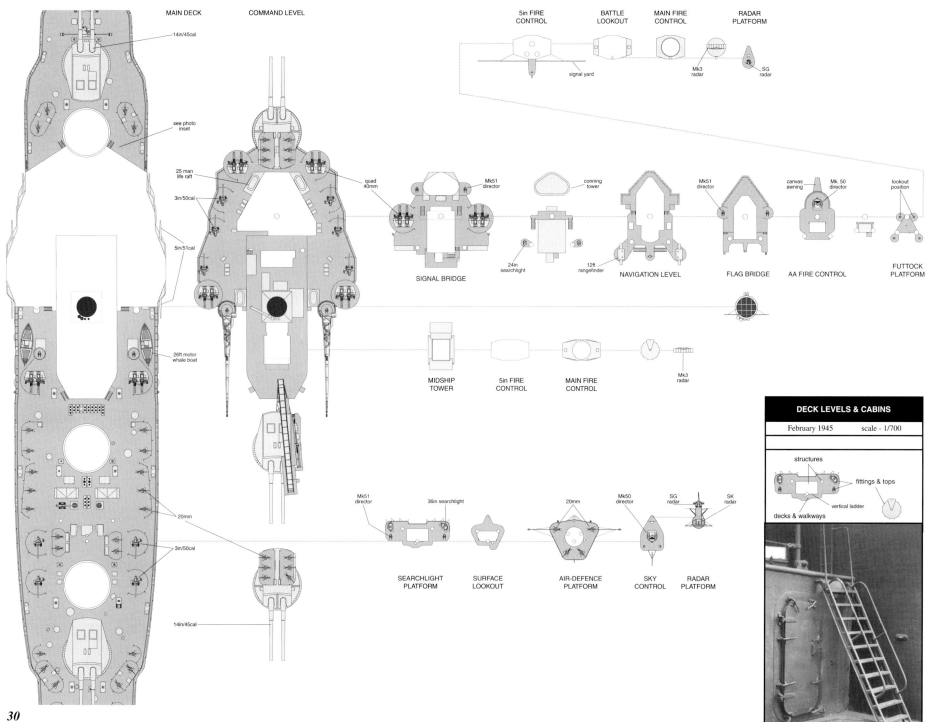

MAIN DECK

COMMAND LEVEL

14in/45cal

see photo
inset

25 man
life raft

3in/50cal

5in/51cal

26ft motor
whale boat

20mm

3in/50cal

14in/45cal

quad
40mm

5in FIRE
CONTROL

BATTLE
LOOKOUT

MAIN FIRE
CONTROL

RADAR
PLATFORM

signal yard

Mk3
radar

SG
radar

Mk51
director

conning
tower

Mk51
director

canvas
awning

Mk. 50
director

lookout
position

24in
searchlight

12ft
rangefinder

SIGNAL BRIDGE

NAVIGATION LEVEL

FLAG BRIDGE

AA FIRE CONTROL

FUTTOCK
PLATFORM

MIDSHIP
TOWER

5in FIRE
CONTROL

MAIN FIRE
CONTROL

Mk3
radar

Mk51
director

36in searchlight

20mm

Mk50
director

SG
radar

SK
radar

SEARCHLIGHT
PLATFORM

SURFACE
LOOKOUT

AIR-DEFENCE
PLATFORM

SKY
CONTROL

RADAR
PLATFORM

DECK LEVELS & CABINS

February 1945   scale - 1/700

structures

fittings & tops

vertical ladder

decks & walkways

30

February, 1940: Havana, Cuba - Infamous Morro Castle looms in the background as the Texas *enters Havana Harbor. Although assigned to Atlantic convoy duty to protect the East Coast, she is still wearing pre-war paint. Colors were Standard Navy Gray on all vertical surfaces and Standard Deck Gray on all horizontal metal surfaces. The teakwood covered decks were left unpainted. The spotter float planes on the catapult are Curtis SOC Seagulls.*

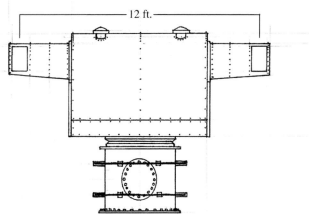

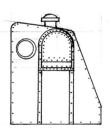

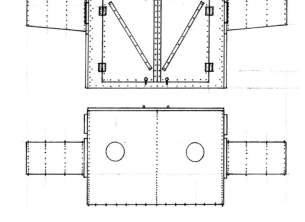

12 ft. Rangefinder

Stereoscopic rangefinders were developed in the 1920s by the US Navy for use as secondary battery directors and to spot the fall of shot for all weapons. They were constructed in 12, 15 and 20 ft. varieties. Texas carried both 12 and 20 ft. rangefinders.

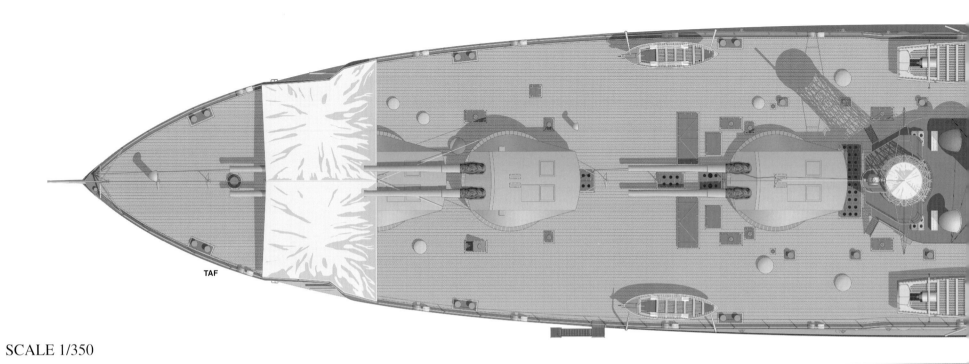

TAF

SCALE 1/350

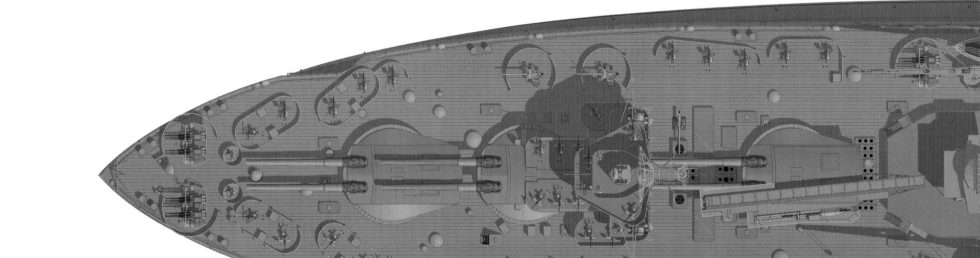

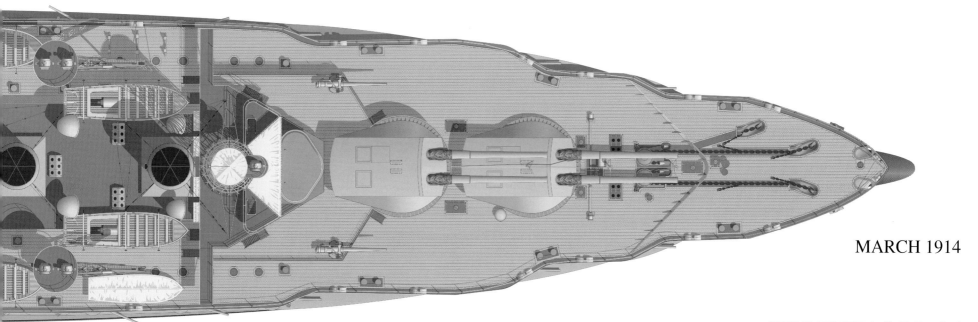

MARCH 1914

USS TEXAS BB-35

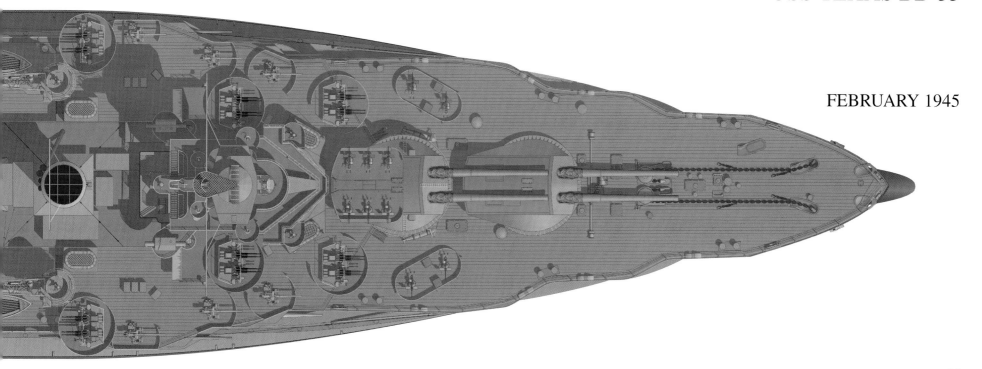

FEBRUARY 1945

July 11, 1942

USN Naval Gun Factory 1.1in. Quad Anti-Aircraft Mount

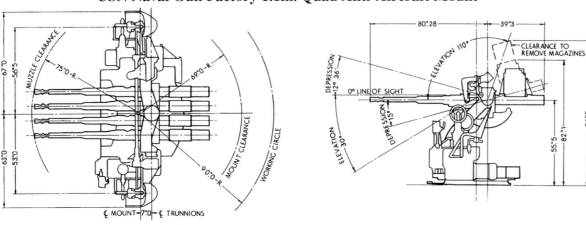

This mount was developed because of the need for a weapon larger than the .50 calibre gun. This mount offered better stopping power, but had many problems with jamming and its overall complexity soon caused cost increases and production delays. This in turn delayed the delivery of the mounts to the US Navy until 1940, at which time the weapon did not possess sufficient stopping power against the latest aircraft. It was common practice for the mount crew to have a ball-peen hammer available to help with the constant jamming problems. Due to production delays, a 3in./50cal. single was temporarily installed in its place during 1940 and 1941. The USN pushed forward with the development of the Swedish Bofors 40mm mount to replace the 1.1in. mount, which was phased out of use on USN capital ships by late 1942.

July 11, 1942 - With America's sudden entry into the war, BB-35 takes on a new role and a new appearance. The new camouflage scheme (Measure 12-modified) is designed to help her blend into the background. Her primary threat however, will come from the skies and the ship has been outfitted accordingly. For the first time, radar has been fitted. A large CXAM-1 screen has been fitted to the fore top, one of only 14 made. Close by, sits a long rectangular FC radar screen. A similar unit is mounted on the mid-ship defense tower. Later designated Mk3, they were the first radar units designed to assist with main battery fire control.

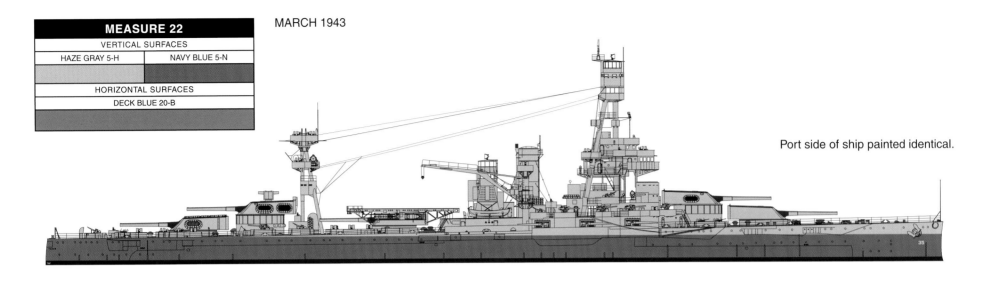

MARCH 1943

MEASURE 22	
VERTICAL SURFACES	
HAZE GRAY 5-H	NAVY BLUE 5-N
HORIZONTAL SURFACES	
DECK BLUE 20-B	

Port side of ship painted identical.

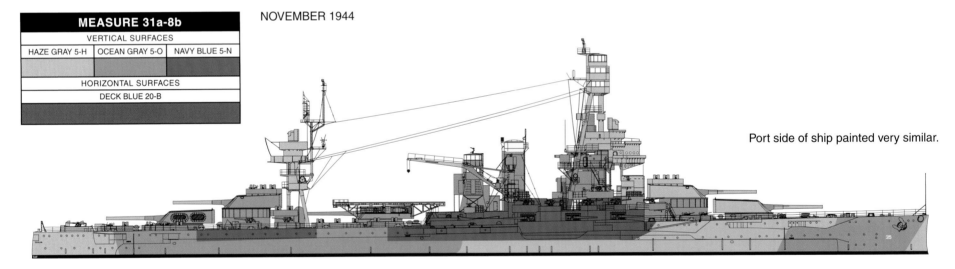

NOVEMBER 1944

MEASURE 31a-8b		
VERTICAL SURFACES		
HAZE GRAY 5-H	OCEAN GRAY 5-O	NAVY BLUE 5-N
HORIZONTAL SURFACES		
DECK BLUE 20-B		

Port side of ship painted very similar.

The color chips below represent the actual shade and intensity of the original paint. The colors of 1941 are a temporary departure from the previous paints in so much as they have no purple/blue chroma. After 1941, the blue/gray vertical surface paint was constructed from a base color of ultramarine blue and black. This would be mixed with white in prescribed proportions to produce the different shades (colors). The two chips on the right were for decks only and were made from different formulas.

LIGHT GRAY (a) 1941   LIGHT GRAY 5-L   HAZE GRAY 5-H   OCEAN GRAY 5-O   SEA BLUE 5-S   NAVY BLUE 5-N   NATURAL TEAK   DARK GRAY (c) 1941   DECK BLUE 20-B

ship scale - 1/700

August 19, 1942: Portsmouth Virginia - Bound for the North African invasion, the Texas has recently received a replacement for the CXAM-1 radar screen on the fore top with a smaller, less bulky SC unit. This unit was found to be unsatisfactory and it too was soon replaced by the improved SC-1 radar. The camouflage appears to have been touched up (note side of #1 turret and in July 11 photos).

Pearl Harbor's tragedy and Midway's miracle both demonstrated the offensive power of the airplane. For her own air defense, Texas *has been fitted with four more 3in guns, four quad 1.1in machine guns and 38 new 20mm Orlikon machine guns. In combat conditions, the ship's small boats will be of little value, taking too long to launch. For the purpose of quick evacuation, numerous 25 and 40 man life rafts are now found all over the ship. These are simply unlashed and thrown overboard. These life rafts were designed with a platform suspended from the flotation ring and survivors actually stood on the suspended platform in chest high water. Extra life lines were provided to allow others to hang on the outside of the raft.*

March 15, 1943 - As the war begins to turn in favor of the Allies, the Texas *assumes a new duty escorting convoys of men and equipment to European theaters and the impending invasions in Africa and France. Hiding a battle ship is tough business so her new camouflage represents an attempt to again confuse enemy submarines with the look of a smaller profile. Anti-aircraft defense has been bolstered with the addition of more 20 mm guns and four additional quad 1.1 in machine guns.*

Massive torpedo bulges added during the 1925-26 refit are well defined from this angle. The idea was to provide a clear space between the outer hull and internal vitals. This clear space was filled with fuel oil, water, stores and other non-critical elements to help absorb a torpedo's explosion. "Fast Battleships" (South Dakota, North Carolina and Iowa Classes) were designed from the beginning with this feature and the immune zone was not so readily visible. Mounted on the foremast above the flag deck is Raytheon Industries first radar unit, the SG surface search.

March 15, 1943

March 15, 1943 - Beautiful aerial photograph shows the multitude of light anti-aircraft positions added in the last two years. All told, 10-3in50s, 32-1.1in and 38 single 20mm machine guns. The Measure 22 camouflage she now wears calls for Deck Blue (20-B) on all decks and horizontal surfaces. This dark blue gray became almost universally applied to the decks of US Navy warships. The hull was painted Navy Blue (5-N) from the boot top to the lowest point in her sheer line. Further up on the hull and all other vertical surfaces were painted Haze Gray (5-H). 20mm gun positions have been added to the mainmast top with two more just below with a pair of 36in search lights. Further down the mainmast, is the box shaped aft conning station. A 12ft rangefinder still sits off center on #4 14in turret. This photo was possibly taken from one of her own Kingfisher spotter aircraft.

40-MM MOUNT, MARK 2 ALL MODS.

40-MM, ANTIAIRCRAFT, QUAD, OPEN OR SHIELDED, BASE RING TYPE

Note: Assembly number of mount is required for precise information. For assembly numbers see:
INDEX SKETCH 94890

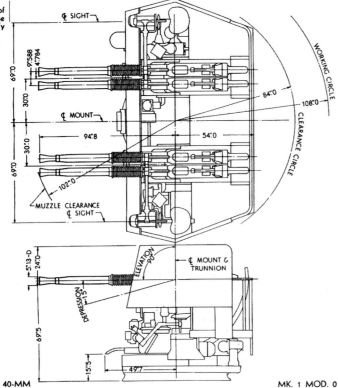

GUN BARRELS—FOUR 40-MM		MK. 1 MOD. 0
40-MM MACHINE GUN MECHANISMS		TWO MK. 1 MODS. 0, 1, 2* OR 3* AND
		TWO MK. 1 MODS. 0, 1, 2* OR 3*
INSTALLATION FOR		COMBAT SHIPS AND LARGER AUXILIARIES
MOUNT MARK 2 MODS.	2, 6, 9, 11,	5, 8, 10, 12,
	13, 14, 17, 18,	15, 16, 19, 20,
	21*, 23*, 25*,	22*, 24*, 26*,
	27*, 29*, 31*.	28*, 30*, 32*.
SHIELD	NONE	MK. 3 & MODS.
SHIELD THICKNESS	—	.375 IN.
		Weights below are approximate
TOTAL WEIGHT OF ASSEMBLY	23,200 LBS.	24,900 LBS.
	*24,900 LBS.	*26,600 LBS.
WEIGHT OF SHIELD		1,700 LBS.
OSCILLATING WEIGHT, four guns		4,550 LBS.
		*5,700 LBS.
RECOILING WEIGHT, per gun		490 LBS.
BRAKE LOAD, per gun		4,800 LBS.

* Asterisk indicates equipment supporting parts of and controlled by gun fire control system Mods. of Mk. 63. (Mounts Mk. 2 Mods. 21–32.)

40-MM QUAD, MARK 2 ALL MODS.

20

20-MM MOUNT, MARK 4 ALL MODS.

20-MM, ANTIAIRCRAFT, SINGLE MOUNT, SHIELDED, PEDESTAL TYPE

Note: Assembly number of mount is required for precise information. For assembly numbers see:
INDEX SKETCH 103308

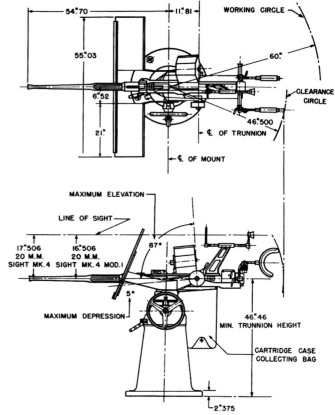

GUN BARREL—20-MM	MK. 4 MODS. 0 OR 1
20-MM MACHINE GUN MECHANISM	MK. 2 MOD. 0 OR MK. 4 MOD. 0
MAGAZINE	MK. 2 MOD. 0 OR MK. 4 MOD. 0
SHIELD	MK. 4 MODS. 0 OR 1
SHIELD THICKNESS	.5 IN.
	Weights below are approximate
TOTAL WEIGHT OF ASSEMBLY	1,695 LBS.
WEIGHT OF SHIELD	250 LBS.
BRAKE LOAD	1,785 LBS.

20-MM, MARK 4 ALL MODS.

6

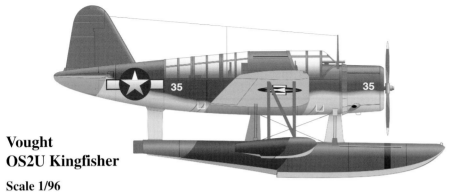

**Vought
OS2U Kingfisher**

Scale 1/96

February 1944 - Although undated, it is reasonably certain this photo was taken shortly after the February 1944 refit prior to the invasion of Normandy. 20mm guns have been removed from the upper bridge area and the main mast top. These and more have been crammed onto the tops of #2 & #4 14in turrets. Two Kingfishers sit in their usual stowage position, lashed on the catapult. The Texas *probably was first assigned her Kingfishers out of a batch of 158 delivered in 1941.*

February 1944 - The early year refit also included the installations of ten quad 40mm mounts, replacing the 1.1in guns, which were troublesome and undercalibered. The Swedish Bofors 40mm, licensed to the US, was a superb medium anti-aircraft gun used by both the US Army and the Navy. On board ship, the usual configuration was in pairs or most often, quadruple mountings. The gun was harder hitting, had a longer range and was much more dependable than the 1.1in gun. Note the bins under #2 14in turret which hold "floater-nets", rope netting with many small flotation blocks. Should the ship be sinking, they would simply be thrown overboard, providing immediate but light duty flotation assistance.

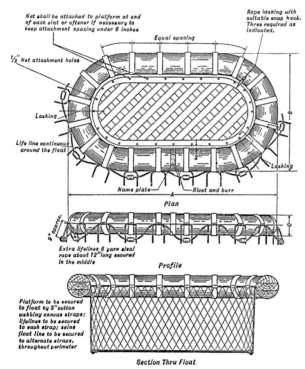

SIZES						
Capacity in Persons	*Dimensions			No. of Wood Floats	Pounds (Approx.)	
	A	B	C		Weight	Buoyancy
10	7'0"	3'6"	10"	8	150	400
15	8'6"	4'0"	11"	8	200	600
25	10'0"	5'6"	12"	10	300	1000
40	11'6"	7'0"	14"	10	450	1600
60	13'0"	8'6"	16"	12	600	2400

*Dimensions shown are approximate. Each float to provide net gravitational buoyant support of 40 pounds per person capacity.

February 1944: Casco Bay, Maine. High atop the main mast, sits a new SK air search radar antenna. This unit was the standard aircraft detection unit aboard US capital ships from 1943 on. It was capable of picking up the image of a medium bomber at 100nm. Just below, a small SG surface search radar.

Late 1944 - The Texas takes on yet another camouflage scheme, a dazzle pattern, Measure 31A-8B. This design called for Navy Blue, Ocean Gray and Haze Gray in large geometric blocks from the boot topping up. The deck and horizontal surfaces: 20-B. Above the new aft 20mm platform, a small Mk50 director has been fitted to aid 3in gun fire. The two 36in search lights have been lowered to a new platform just forward of #4 turret in company with a pair of Mk51 40mm gun directors.

Late 1944 - This photograph probably finds Texas *on her way from California to Pearl Harbor and her first Pacific assignment: Iwo Jima. Another Mk50 sits forward on the flag bridge and a small canvas cover is stretched over the front of the navigation deck to give shade to bridge personnel.*

February 1945: East China Sea - Well known photo taken from the stern of the battleship Nevada BB-36 *shows* Texas *with a massive Allied build-up off Iwo Jima. She comes repainted for the occasion in Measure 21:overall Navy Blue (5-N) on the vertical and, of course, Deck Blue on the horizontal surfaces. It makes for a dark form on a dark ocean and hopefully a difficult target for the Japanese last desperate defense, the Kamikaze. As old as she was, the* Texas *and other older sisters had been slowly transformed into ideal bombardment platforms, including good anti-aircraft defenses. A"dazzled" Fletcher class destroyer cutting behind the* Texas *helps with AA duties.*

February 15, 1945: East China Sea - A Kingfisher prepares to launch prior to the Texas' first action against Japan; pre invasion bombardment of the island of Iwo Jima. The 0S2U had a range of about 800nm which meant the spotter could direct fire for over 41/2 hours at a time. It could also deliver two small bombs. Texas will turn her 14in and 5in guns on Iwo Jima for the next nine days.

January 14, 1948: Hawkins Point, Baltimore, Maryland - The USS Texas *is assisted from her birth in the "Mothball Fleet" to begin the journey to San Jacinto, Texas. Here she will be recommissioned, this time, to become Flagship of the Texas Navy and permanent memorial to all who fought on the seas of the Second World War.*

May 30, 1989: Galveston, Texas - Dramatic photograph of Texas *in a floating drydock at Todd Shipyard in the midst of a lengthy restoration. From December 13, 1988 to February 23, 1990, major reconstruction and structural repairs took 175 tons of new steel at a cost nearing 7 million dollars.*

GENERAL STATISTICS

Authorized
June 24, 1910

Builder
Newport News
Shipbuilding & Drydock Co.

Keel Laid
April 17, 1911

Launched
May 18, 1912

Commissioned
March 12, 1914

Dimensions (ft)

	1914	1945
length overall	573.00	573.00
beam	95.25	106.00
draught (min.)	28.50	28.50
(max.)	29.75	32.25

Displacement (tons)

standard	1914	27,000
	1945	30,350
full load	1914	28,400
	1945	34,000

Armor (in)
main belt ....10 to 12
decks ....1.5 to 4
turrets ....4 to 9
  face 14
bulkheads ....9 to 11
barbettes ....5 to 12
conning tower ....4 to 12

Propulsion
1914
Boilers ....Babcock & Wilcox (14)
Engines ....Vertical-inverted 4 cylinder
   triple expansion
   Manufactured by the builder.
Speed ....21 kts @ 28,000 shp
Fuel ....3000 tons (coal)
   400 tons (oil)
1945
Boilers ....Bureau Express type (6)
Engines ....as built
Speed ....20.5 kts @ 28,000 shp
Fuel ....5200 tons (oil)

Complement
1914 ....58 officers, 944 enlisted men
1945 ....98 officers, 1625 enlisted men

Aircraft
1914-18 no facilities
1919-25 Sopwith Camel
   Nieuport 28
   Harriot HD-2
1926-30 Vought FU-1
1931-38 Vought 03u Corsair
1938-41 Curtiss SOC Seagull
1941-45 Vought-Sikorsky OS2U Kingfisher

Endurance
1914............9,600 nm @ 10 kts
   3,700 nm @ 20 kts
1945...........15,400 nm @ 10 kts
   6,500 nm @ 18 kts

Recommissioned
April 21, 1948
San Jacinto Park, Texas

Cost to build
$10.5 million (1914)

ARMAMENT SUMMARY

		1914	1917	1927	1941	1942	1943	1944	1945
main battery	14in/45cal	10	10	10	10	10	10	10	10
secondary battery	5in/51cal	21	16	16	6	6	6	6	6
anti-aircraft	3in/50cal	–	8	8	8 to 10	10	10	10	10
	40mm	–	–	–	–	–	–	40	40
	1.1in	–	–	–	16	16 to 32	32	32-0	–
	20mm	–	–	–	16	16 to 38	38	42 to 44	44
	.50cal	–	–	–	8	–	–	–	–
torpedo tubes	21in	4	4	–	–	–	–	–	–

REFERENCES

Battleship & Cruiser Aircraft of the US Navy
W. Larkins, Schiefer Publications, 1996

Battleship Texas
H. Power, Jr., Texas A&M University Press, 1993

Dictionary of American Naval Fighting Ships
US Government Printing Office, 1990

Naval Radar
N. Friedman, Conway Maritime Press Ltd., 1981

Naval Weapons of WWII
J. Campbell, Conway Maritime Press Ltd., 1985

U.S. Battleships: A Design History
N. Friedman, Naval Institute Press, 1985

US Naval Weapons
N. Friedman, Naval Institute Press, 1985

US Navy Camouflage of the WWII Era
L. Sowinski & T. Walkowiak, Floating Drydock, 1976

RESOURCES

U. S. Naval Historical Center
Building 57, 805 Kidder Breese St. SE,
Washington Navy Yard, Washington DC, 20374-2571
(202)433-2765 • Web site: www.history.navy.mil

U. S. National Archives - Archives II
8601 Adelphi Rd., College Park, MD. 20740-6001
(301)713-6800 • Web site: www.nara.gov

U. S. Naval Institute
291 Wood Rd., Annapolis, MD 21402-5034
(800)233-8764 • Web site: www.usni.org

ACKNOWLEDGMENTS

Classic Warships
would like to express its gratitude to the following individuals
Tom Freeman • Margarita Marders
Don Montgomery • Steve Barker
Don Preul & Jeanne Pollard
A. D. Baker III • Edward Morrison
Ed Finney, Rob Hanshew & Chuck Haberlein, Jr.
@ US Naval Historical Center

WARSHIP PICTORIAL SERIES

available at the time of this printing
W. P. # 4 USS Texas BB-35
W. P. # 9 Yorktown Class Carriers
W. P. #10 Indianapolis & Portland
W. P. #14 USS Wichita CA-45
W. P. #18 USS New Mexico BB-40
W. P. #19 KM Bismarck
W. P. #20 HMS Hood
W. P. #22 USS Ticonderoga CV/CVA/CVS-14
W. P. #23 Italian Heavy Cruisers of WWII
W. P. #24 Arleigh Burke Class Destroyers
W. P. #26 KM Tirpitz
W. P. #27 KM Type VII U-boats

Front Cover: Painting "The Pacific Lone Star," battleship *USS Texas* bombards enemy positions on Mt. Suribachi, Iwo Jima on the morning of February 15, 1945.

Back Cover: Painting "Reporting for Duty," one of America's newest dreadnoughts, *USS Texas BB-35* leads the US Fleet into Scapa Flow to rendezvous with the British Grand Fleet in February 1918.

Cover Art Provided
by
TOM FREEMAN
SM & S NAVAL PRINTS
P. O. Box 41 • Forest Hills, MD 21050-0041
Ph. (410)893-8184 • Fx. (410)879-1261
Web Site: www.tomfreemanart.com

The *USS Texas BB-35* lives on as the only remaining dreadnought battleship from the First World War and one of only a few remaining from the Second World War. This mighty warship offers the visitor a trip into naval history. Beginning in 1914 as one of world's most powerful ships to her indispensible service in the Second World War, her career paralleled the rise and fall of the dreadnought, a time when the battleships ruled the seas. The Memorial is open to the general public throughout the year. You may contact the museum through the following address;

BATTLESHIP TEXAS FOUNDATION

3527 Battleground Road
La Porte, Texas 77571
(281)479-2431